™

series editors
JOHN WEEKS &
EDWARD MARTIN III

collection editor
LYNN ADAIR

collection design manager
BRIAN GOGOLIN

collection designer
SCOTT FUENTES

BUBBLEGUM CRISIS GRAND MAL

story • pencils • inks
ADAM WARREN

additional inks
ROBERT DEJESUS
HARRY CANDELARIO
DAVE JOHNSON
TOM RANEY
KARL STORY
BRAD VANCATA

colors
JOE ROSAS

lettering

with an introduction by
KENICHI SONODA

BUBBLEGUM CRISIS™ GRAND MAL

Published by Manga Publishing Ltd., 40 St Peters Road, London W6 9BD. First edition published September 1995. No part of this publication may be reproduced or transmitted by any means, electronic, mechanical, photocopying or otherwise, without the prior permission of the Publisher.

British Library Cataloguing in Publication Data. A catalogue record for this book is available from the British Library.

ISBN 1 900097 02 8

Adam's slow and steady efforts at drawing
otaku*-type manga have once again borne fruit!
Although Bubblegum Crisis is just a fond
memory to me now, it gives me great pleasure
to see the characters I designed make their
appearance in America.

Good job, Adam!
Keep on drawing!
I'm behind you all the way!

*dedicated fan

園田健一

—Kenichi Sonoda

(Who has been mired in the depths of Doom for three months now . . .)

CHAPTER ONE

DAMN IT.

--BEGINNING OUR FINAL APPROACH TO *NARITA INTERNATIONAL AIRPORT*--

THANK YOU FOR FLYING JAPAN AIRLINES--

ALMOST MADE IT THROUGH THE FLIGHT.

--A SUBSIDIARY OF *GENOM DEVELOPMENT CORPORATION!*

OCCUPIED

SO MUCH FOR MEDICATION.

FIRST, THE SUDDEN *EUPHORIC* STATE SWEEPS OVER ME.

THAT'S THE *REALLY* ANNOYING PART, HAVING TO FEEL *HAPPY* ABOUT THIS...

NEXT COME THE *CHILLS*--

--RIGHT ON SCHEDULE.

ANYTIME NOW--

--THE HALLUCINATIONS SHOULD KICK IN.

--LET GENOM BRING IN FOREIGN- ERS--

--OR EVEN THESE *BOOMER* THINGS--!

WE NEED *HELP* HERE--

VIDEO SAMPLE

"*GENOM* DEVELOPMENT CORPORATION SPEARHEADS RECONSTRUCTION EFFORT."--*BEIJING BUSINESS JOURNAL*

"AFTER PREYING ON THE REELING GIANTS OF CORPORATE JAPAN--"

"*GENOM* TARGETS PREY OVERSEAS."--*COMMERCENET NEWS SERVICE*

"WHO THE HELL IS *GENOM?*" --U.S. PRESIDENT *DEIRDRE SHAW*

VIDEO SAMPLE

IN ORDER TO ACCELERATE OUR *URBAN RECLAMATION* PROJECTS--

--NOT TO MENTION THE COMPLETION OF OUR *GENOM TOWER* ARCOLO- GY--

--WE'RE PLANNING LIMITED USAGE OF OUR *BEST- KNOWN* PROD- UCT--

--THE *BOOMER.*

"WHAT'S A *BOOMER,* MOMMY?"

"WELL, HONEY..."

SUBJECT: "PRISS."

FULL NAME PRISCILLA S. ASAGIRI, AGE 18.

OCCUPATION: ROCK (RETROTHRASH) SINGER.

"--MAKES UP FOR IN INTENSITY WHAT SHE LACKS IN ORIGINAL-ITY--"—ANONYMOUS REVIEW OF LIVE PER-FORMANCE BY PRISS AND THE REPLICANTS"

"ADMITTEDLY, PRISS IS SOMEWHAT OF AN UN-GUIDED MISSILE."

"DOWN THE ROAD, HER INSTABILITY MAY POSE SERIOUS PROBLEMS..."

"...BUT FOR NOW, HER CAPACITY FOR VIOLENCE MAKES HER QUITE USEFUL."
—SYLIA STINGRAY

"--WHAT, IF I DON'T THINK *GENOM* IS '*ALL-GOOD* AND DESERVING OF *ALL MY LOVE*'--"

"--AND *SAY SO*--"

"--THEN PEOPLE SAY I'M '*TOO POLITICAL*'?"

"THEY CAN JUST *GO TO HELL*--"

—PRISS, IN INTERVIEW WITH WAJLEMAC MUSIC 'ZINE

VIDEO SAMPLE

C'MON, PRISS, YOU *RAGE-AHOLIC*...!

DO SOMETHING *ANGRY* AND *UNHINGED*!

VIDEO SAMPLE

SHOW US WHAT A *WILD REBEL* YOU ARE!

THAT'S MORE LIKE IT--

EXCERPT FROM COUNSELING SESSION (MANDATED BY PLEA BARGAIN ON ASSAULT CHARGES):

THERAPIST: "THAT'S QUITE A LOAD OF *UNHEALTHY ANGER* YOU'RE CARRYING THERE, PRISS..."

PRISS: "⇒*BLEEP*⇐ YOU."

EXCERPT FROM CONVERSATION RECORDED BETWEEN *AD POLICE* OFFICERS:

"HEY *LEON*..."

"...CHECK *THIS* OUT."

DISCTEK HR-120
HIGH DENSITY OPTICAL-STORAGE MEMORY MODULE

"WE GOT SIGHTINGS OF, QUOTE, *'WEIRD MECHS'* IN THE RE-CLAMATION ZONES."

"WHAT, SOME *NEW* TYPE OF BOOMER?"

"NAH, DON'T THINK SO..."

"THESE THINGS'RE SUPPOSED TO LOOK KIND OF *JURY-RIGGED*..."

"...Y'KNOW, *PIECED TOGETHER*."

SUBJECT: *SYLIA STINGRAY,* AGE 21.

OFFICIAL RECORDS, BIRTH TO AGE 15, LOST IN 2025 EARTHQUAKE.

OCCUPATION LISTED AS "OWNER/OPERATOR, *'SILKY DOLL'* LINGERIE SHOP" ON 2030 INCOME TAX RETURN.

KONYA WA "*HURRICANE*"♫

CONTROLS *SUBSTANTIAL* FINANCIAL AND REAL ESTATE HOLDINGS--

--*NOT* DETAILED ON 2030 INCOME TAX RETURN.

MŌ ICHIDO "*HURRICANE*"--♫

HEY, SIS--

THESE MOTOROID *SENSOR SUITES* GOT MESSED UP IN TRAN-SIT...!

IT'LL TAKE A DAY OR TWO TO *RECALIBRATE* 'EM...

FINE, *MACKIE.*

--GET A CLOSE-UP ON *SYLIA* HERE, *MACKIE*--!

"HI! I'M OL' *ENIGMATIC* SYLIA!"

"WHY, I'M A *MYSTERY* OF TWO *CONUNDRUMS* OF A *RIDDLE* OF *ANOTHER* MYSTERY--"

NENE DEAR, YOU'RE GETTING *OUT OF HAND*--

ECHO FIVE-FIVE TO ADPOLICE DISPATCH--

--GOT A BOOMER SPOTTED--

--A COMBAT MODEL--

VIDEO SAMPLE

--CREATOR OF SO-CALLED "BOOMER TECHNOLOGY," DR. STINGRAY WAS SLAIN TODAY IN--

--BOOMER'S IN FLIGHT--

--HEADED OUT OF RECLAMATION ZONE EIGHT--

--DAMN IT--!

HANDLE WITH CARE

THE BOOMER'S GOING INTO A POPULATED AREA--

--BETTER WHISTLE UP THE GUNSHIPS, DISPATCH--

VIDEO SAMPLE

--SURVIVED BY DAUGHTER SYLIA, TWELVE, AND SON MACKIE, FIVE--

--THIS IS GONNA GET UGLY--

GET THE TRUCK, MACKIE.

I'LL CONTACT THE OTHERS--

--IT'S FINALLY LANDED, DISPATCH--

WE'RE VECTORING IN WHISKEY SQUADRON, ECHO FIVE-FIVE--

--JUST KEEP YOUR DISTANCE, FROM THE BOGEY--

HELL, IT MAY BE A COMBAT MODEL--

--BUT IT HASN'T SHOWN ANY FIRE-POWER YET--

VIDEO SAMPLE

JOIN THE ELITE!

JOIN THE ADVEN-TURE!

Join the ADPolice!

HRAAAA

OH SHIT--

VIDEO SAMPLE

LIKE YOUR POLICE FORCE OVERBEARING, OVERBUDGETED AND OVERARMED?

WELL, OUR VERY OWN "ADVANCED POLICE" SHOULD BE JUST WHAT YOU'RE--

WHROOM

KEYAM--

VIDEO SAMPLE

KILLED IN ACTION

029	2030	2031
TSUYA EGAWA	TSUKASA DOKITE	NG MUI
FUJISHIMA	JAMES ELLROY	CHOW YUN FAT
KLUTE	KERSON HUANG
INOSANTO	THOM JONES
HATSUMI	KEVIN J. SLEET
ROTHROCK	DREXLER
ASH	ORTON
JOYCE G	NDEZ
CHUNG	SHO FU	DA
SHIROW	TSUI H	HI
ASANISHIKI	YAMA	KA
MORENO	DENIS	KA
REYES	GLOV	TREC
AKAHAS		

LOOK AT THAT LIST--

--TELL ME AGAIN HOW BLEEP-ING OVER-ARMED WE ARE--

--ECHO FIVE-FIVE'S DOWN-- --BURNING IN THE STREET--

--TO TAC SQUADS, FROM GUNSHIP PILOTS TO DISPATCHERS--

--WE'RE ALL PULLING TOGETHER FOR YOUR SAFETY!

36
ADP
05

VIDEO SAMPLE

ADPOLICE

"--THE 'ADVANCED POLICE SPECIAL CRIMES CONTROL UNIT,' FORMED IN 2027 TO COMBAT 'BOOMER CRIME' AND SIMILAR THREATS--" --"SAY 'HI' TO THE ADPOLICE!" (PR VIDEO)

--APCS CHARLIE NINE-ONE AND NINE-THREE--

--SET UP A PERIMETER AT THE INTER-SECTION OF KOSUGI AND QUINCY--

SUBJECT: NENE ROMANOVA, AGE 17 (LISTED AS AGE 20 IN ADPOLICE FILE).

SYLIA-- --ARE YOU GETTING THIS--

OCCUPATION: ADPOLICE "COMMUNICA-TIONS SUPPORT SPECIALIST."

--LITTLE MISS CYBER-PUNK--♪

HACKING INTO YOUR POOR UNSUS-PECTING BOSSES' COMPUTERS--!

MAYBE THAT'S WHY THEY HAVEN'T WISED UP AND FIRED YOU YET--!

THAT'S NOT TRUE--

VIDEO SAMPLE

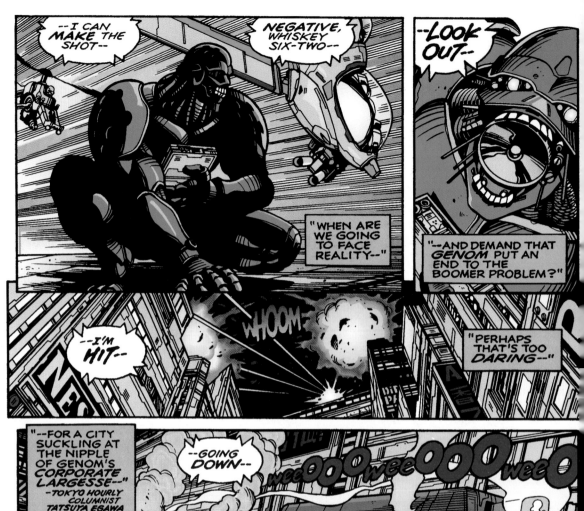

--I CAN MAKE THE SHOT--

NEGATIVE, WHISKEY SIX-TWO--

--LOOK OUT--

"WHEN ARE WE GOING TO FACE REALITY--"

"--AND DEMAND THAT GENOM PUT AN END TO THE BOOMER PROBLEM?"

"PERHAPS THAT'S TOO DARING--"

--I'M HIT--

WHOOM

"--FOR A CITY SUCKLING AT THE NIPPLE OF GENOM'S CORPORATE LARGESSE--"
-TOKYO HOURLY COLUMNIST TATSUYA EGAWA

--GOING DOWN--

I DON'T NEED TO LOOK OUT THE WINDOW--

--TO KNOW A BOOMER IS CAPERING ABOUT UP THERE.

AND I REALLY DON'T NEED TO SEE ONE JUST YET.

I'LL BE RUNNING INTO BOOMERS AGAIN SOON ENOUGH--

PHITNESS utopia

BE FRE

SUBJECT: LINNA YAMAZAKI, AGE 19.

OCCUPATION: FITNESS INSTRUCTOR.

PLACED SECOND, WOMENS' DIVISION, IN OPEN TAI CHI CHUAN FORMS COMPETITION AT 2029 WORLD KUOSHO TOURNAMENT.

WON TITLE OF TOHATO™ "ALL-RAISIN PRINCESS" IN 2027 "ALL-RAISIN BEAUTY PAGEANT."

YANG-ST TAI CHI

CHOY Li FUT

TAI NTIS

JEET KUNE DO

VIDEO SAMPLE

OH, YEAH--! TEACHING TAI CHI AND STEP TRAINING TO A BUNCH OF FLAB-OIDS--!

THAT'S A FULFILLING CAREER, ALL RIGHT--

VIDEO SAMPLE

HEY, AT LEAST I'M NOT TOTALLY USE-LESS IN A FIGHT!

AND SPEAKING OF FLAB-OIDS--

♪--ANATA NI "HURRICANE"--♪

--TSUTAETAI No "LOVING YOU"--

Silky Doll FINE LINGERIE

SKREEE

NEED A RIDE, MISS...?

--HE'S *OFF THE TRAIN*--

--*TAG HIM, TAG HIM*--

AS A MATTER OF FACT, *YES*--

COOL.

--OFFICERS *WONG* AND *MACNICHOL* RESPONDING, DISPATCH--

JEEZ, THOSE HELO JOCKEYS 'RE SURE TAKING A *BEATING* TONIGHT--!

THE ADP'S *ALWAYS* TAKING A BEATING, *LEON.*

IT'S OUR *ROLE IN LIFE.*

YEAH...

...ESPECIALLY IF YOU'RE A *TAC SQUAD* GRUNT, REMEMBER?

PLINKING AT BOOMERS WITH *ASSAULT RIFLES...*

≥SNORT≤

NO WONDER WE DIDN'T DO SO WELL, SOMETIMES--

VIDEO SAMPLE

--HER *ARM*--

--WE GOTTA FIND HER *ARM,* GODDAMMIT--

I'M TELLING YOU, *DALEY*--

...IT TAKES *SERIOUS* HARDWARE TO TACKLE BOOMERS.

"YOU GOTTA FIGHT HIGH TECH--"

"--WITH HIGH TECH--"

--VIDEOTAPED IN FLIGHT OVER THE *NEW ROPPONGI* DISTRICT--

--MATCHES NO KNOWN TYPE OF *BOOMER* OR--

"--CLEARLY *POWERED ARMOR* OF SOME SORT--"

"--BUT WHO'S WEARING IT?"
—TOKYO HOURLY

"KNIGHT SABERS"--?

WHO THE *BLEEP* IS *THAT*--

'--GROUP CALLING THEMSELVES THE *"KNIGHT SABERS"* PUT AN END TO YESTERDAY'S *BOOMER RAMPAGE*--'
—UNIVERSAL MEDIA NETWEB (TOKYO)

"HIGH-TECH *VIGILANTES:* A LOOK AT MEGA-TOKYO'S SHADOWY *'KNIGHT SABERS.'"
—*PACIFICA NEWSNET*

"RUMORS OF *'KNIGHT SABERS'* IN-VOLVEMENT IN *'CORPORATE MERCENARY'* ACTIVITY... MORE TONIGHT AT ELEVEN."
—*UNIVERSAL MEDIA NETWEB (TOKYO)*

--LOST IT?

WELL, IT'S GOT TO BE AROUND HERE SOME-WHERE--

--THEY DON'T CARRY ENOUGH *FUEL* TO GET--

--DEPLOYING *HIGH-RES INFRARED ARRAY*--

--COME OUT, COME OUT, *WHEREVER YOU ARE*--

--HOLD ON--

--WE'RE PICKING UP A CODED TRANSMISSION, *STRONG*--

--GOTTA BE THE *BOOMER* SIGNALLING FOR *HELP,* OR--

--GIVE ME A *FIX* ON IT, NOW--

HEY ≤SKRKK≥

≤KRKK≥ SOMEBODY'S *JAMMING* HIM--

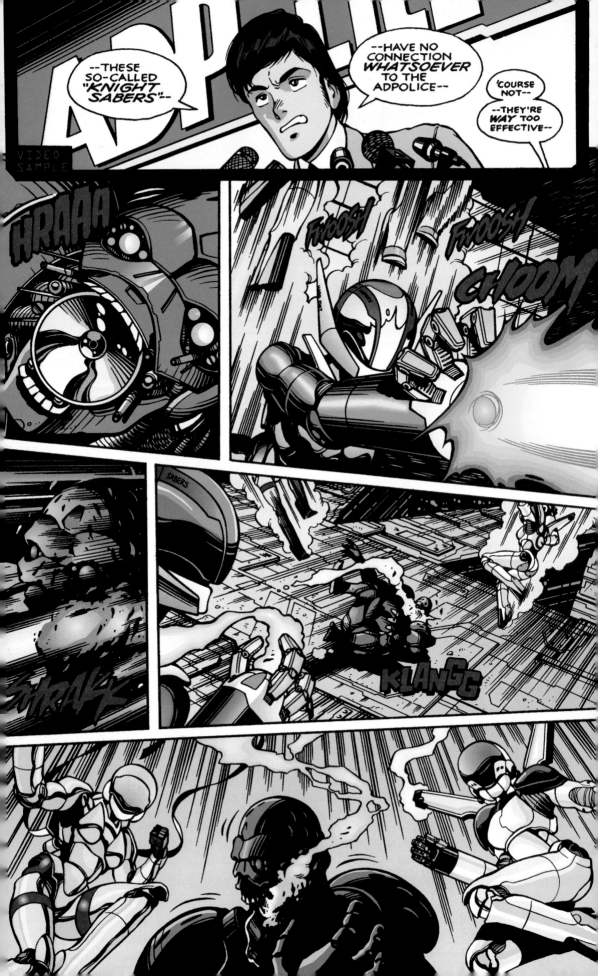

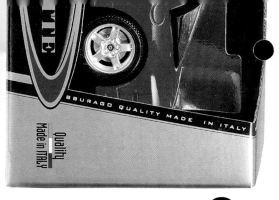

BBURAGO QUALITY MADE IN ITALY

Quality
Made in ITALY

3

GOLD
COLLECTION

1/18

1/16

COD. 3301
With permission of RENAULT

ALPINE A 110 (1972)

NEW

1/18

COD. 3315
Manufactured with permission of
PORSCHE A.G.

PORSCHE 911 CARRERA (1997)

NEW

bura

4

WHIRR

KLAK

BETTER LIVING
THROUGH MECHATRONICS.
GENOM
図

"YO! *NENE!*"

"YOU GOING
DOWN TO
FORENSICS,
BABE?"

"OH, HI,
LEON...!"

"UM, I'M
HEADED TO
*COMP/
ANALYSIS,*
ACTUALLY."

"WELL,
BETTER
LET ME
ESCORT
YOU."

ZZZKKS

YOU KNOW HOW
THOSE *TECHIES*
BEHAVE AROUND
PRETTY GIRLS
LIKE YOURSELF!

THE COMPUTER
JOCKS ARE
PROBABLY TOO
BUSY TO HASSLE
YOU *TODAY,*
THOUGH.

HUH...

...I'VE
NOTICED...

UPSTAIRS
WANTS THAT
LOOSE END
FROM LAST
NIGHT'S BOOMER
INCIDENT
WRAPPED UP,
ASAP...

UM...

..."LOOSE END"...?

YEAH. THAT *BOOMER* THE "KNIGHT SABERS" OFFED WAS CARRYING SOME KIND OF "MEMORY MODULE" THINGAMABOB.

--IT'S GOT AN *INCREDIBLE* COMPRESSION LEVEL--

LAB 3A

--WEIRDEST *CODING* I'VE EVER SEEN--

DISCTEK HR 120
HIGH-DENSITY OPTICAL STORAGE MEMORY MODULE

GUESS THE *"BABES IN ARMOR"* DIDN'T SPOT IT LAST NIGHT, HUH?

OH, *JEEZ*...!

I DIDN'T NOTICE THE STUPID THING...

WHAT'S THAT, NENE?

OH, UH, *NOTHING*...!

DISCTEK HR 120
HIGH-DENSITY OPTICAL STORAGE MEMORY MODULE

--GONNA TAKE *BIG IRON* TO DECRYPT *THIS* SUCKER--

BETTER LET *ADMIN* KNOW THE BAD NEWS--

--BREAKING THIS'LL TAKE A DAY OR TWO, AT LEAST--

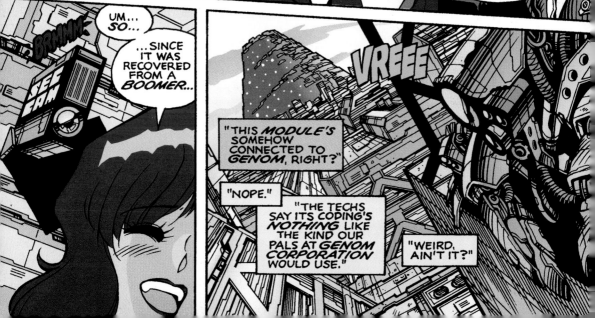

BRMMM

UM... SO...

...SINCE IT WAS RECOVERED FROM A *BOOMER*...

SEE FAM

VREEE

"THIS *MODULE'S* SOMEHOW CONNECTED TO *GENOM*, RIGHT?"

"NOPE."

"THE TECHS SAY ITS CODING'S *NOTHING* LIKE THE KIND OUR PALS AT *GENOM CORPORATION* WOULD USE."

"WEIRD, AIN'T IT?"

QUIXOTE IN A MINISKIRT.

I PARTICULARLY LIKE THE SEARING POLITICAL INSIGHTS OF HER LYRICS...

--C'MON-- SAY IT!

"GENOM SUCKS!

I CAN'T **HEAR** YOU--

HMMF.

SO *THIS* IS SYLIA'S NEWEST ACQUISITION.

VERY *DYNAMIC* ARCHITECTURE...! ⇥SNORT⇤

AND NOT IN A VERY FASHIONABLE *NEIGHBORHOOD*, EITHER...!

OH WELL.

UM... HELLO?

SYLIA? ANYBODY HOME?

双則彩死。

⇥SKRAK⇤

♪HELLO, ♫ MACKIE...!

OH, UH... HI!

COME ON IN, NENE!

--PERHAPS THE MOST *SIGNIFICANT* ASPECT OF DR. STINGRAY'S RESEARCH--

--WAS HIS DEVELOPMENT OF THE BOOMERS' FORM OF *ARTIFICIAL INTELLIGENCE*--

"SYLIA.

"PLEASE PARDON THE *MELODRAMA*...

"...BUT IF YOU ARE HEARING THIS, I HAVE PROBABLY BEEN *MURDERED.*"

--WITH A RESULT *CLOSELY ANALOGOUS* TO HUMAN CONSCIOUSNESS.

EXACTLY *HOW* THIS WAS ACHIEVED REMAINS GENOM'S *TRADE SECRET.*

"I MUST LEAVE *SOME* COUNTER TO GENOM'S CERTAIN *ABUSE* OF MY WORK.

"*YOU* WILL BE THAT COUNTER, SYLIA."

--OF COURSE, WE ARE *FOREVER* INDEBTED TO THE BRILLIANT WORK OF THE LATE *DR. STINGRAY.*

WITHOUT HIS IMPORTANT CONTRIBUTIONS, *GENOM* CORPORATION MIGHT NEVER HAVE--

GENOM EXECUTIVE BOARD CHAIRMAN *QUINCY*

"TO *AID* YOU IN THIS...

"...I HAVE GIVEN YOU AND YOUR BROTHER CERTAIN...*GIFTS,* YOU MIGHT SAY."

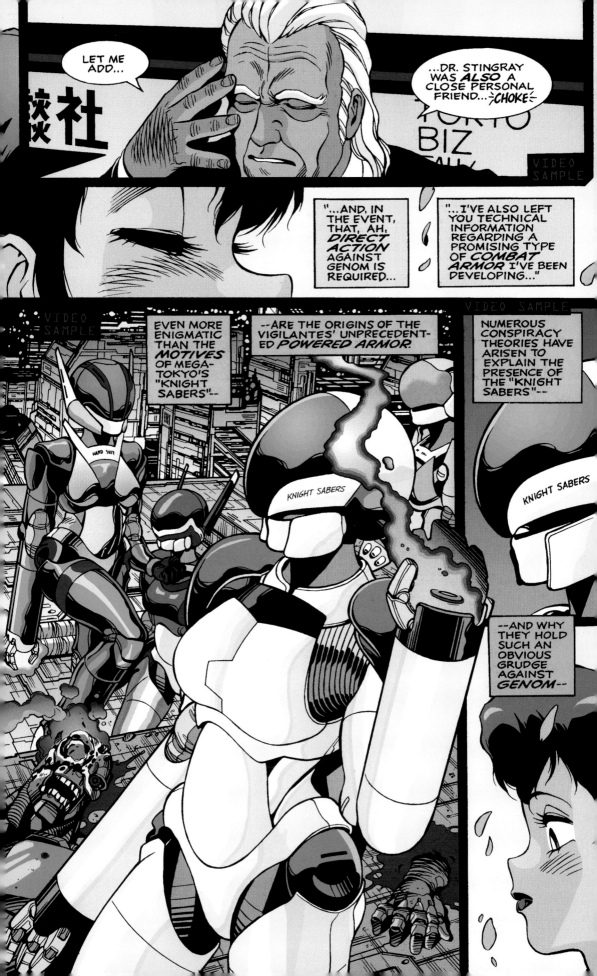

--THE "KNIGHT SABERS" ARE NOTHING MORE THAN *TERRORISTS*, CRIMINALS WHO DESERVE TO BE--

"OH, FATHER..."

"..YOUR UNLIMITED *INTELLECT* CREATED A TECHNOLOGICAL *MIRACLE*..."

"..BUT YOUR FLAWED *JUDGMENT* PLACED IT IN THE HANDS OF AMORAL *THUGS*.

TERMINATE SIMULATION.

"SO YOU *ALTERED* ME, SO THAT I MIGHT SOMEHOW REDEEM THE *TANGLED MESS* YOU LEFT BEHIND.

"NOW, I'M FORCED TO KILL YOUR FIGURATIVE CHILDREN, THE *BOOMERS*, WHEN THEY RUN WILD...

"..WHILE THE MEN WHO PROFIT FROM THEIR ABUSE REMAIN FOREVER *OUT OF MY REACH*.

"FATHER, IF *I* COULD BEAR CHILDREN...

"...I'D WANT TO LEAVE THEM A LESS *HOPELESS* AND *AGONIZING* LEGACY THAN THE ONE YOU LEFT ME."
--EXCERPTS FROM SYLIA STINGRAY'S PRIVATE RECORDS.

WELL, SYLIA *DOES* SEEM TO HAVE MIXED FEELINGS ABOUT DAD.

NOT THAT *I* KNOW WHY...

HMMM... *I* WONDER WHAT—

WHOKK

AKKK-!!

SHOULDN'T PULL *KNIVES* ON PEOPLE IN *MINISKIRTS*, ACE.

IT'S JUST NOT *DONE*, SEE?

OWWWW-!

SORRY, THE URGE TO "*WHITE KNIGHT*" JUST OVERCAME ME.

FEEL FREE TO KICK HIM IN THE HEAD, IF YOU WANT...

NAH.

WOULDN'T WANNA RISK *DIRTYING* MY BOOT ON A *GENOM GROUPIE.*

YOU'RE BREAKIN' MY *ARRM--*

HUH...

I'M NOT TOO BIG A FAN OF GENOM, MYSELF...

HEY, NEITHER IS *ANYBODY* WITH AN *OPERATIVE BRAIN CELL...!*

OWwww...

--FACED WITH A NUBILE, UNDER-DRESSED RETRO-THRASH BABE--

--I JUST HAVE TO GIVE HER AN IMPROMPTU LIFESTYLE CRITIQUE!

--AND **DON'T** COME BACK, YOU **DICK!!!**

La FiLLE plastiqUE lOOK KLUB

VREEE

UNDENIABLY, I AM IN DECLINE.

--YOU'RE *LOSING* IT, NENE!

THIS *MEMORY MODULE* MUST HAVE BEEN PRACTI-CALLY LYING OUT IN THE *OPEN*, AND YOU DIDN'T EVEN *NOTICE* IT!

YOU WERE THERE TOO, *LINNA!*

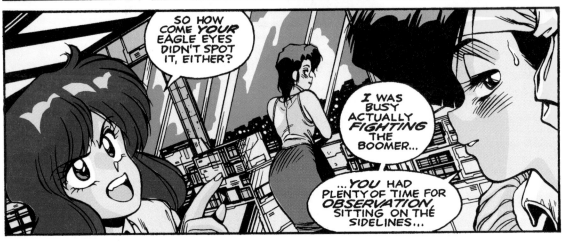

SO HOW COME *YOUR* EAGLE EYES DIDN'T SPOT IT, EITHER?

I WAS BUSY ACTUALLY *FIGHTING* THE BOOMER...

...*YOU* HAD PLENTY OF TIME FOR *OBSERVATION*, SITTING ON THE SIDELINES...

SOME-
THING
IN MY
MOUTH--?

GUCHHK

PTOO

SEVERED
FINGERS.

NOT MINE,
THIS TIME...

THEY'RE
BOTH DEAD...
MANGLED...

THANK YOU,
GENOM.

"AGGRESSIVE
NAÏVETÉ," HUH?

POMPOUS
ASS...!

THE BASTARDS
COULDN'T SEE
FIT TO KILL ME
OUTRIGHT, COULD
THEY--

HUNH.

"POINTLESSLY
SELF-
DESTRUCTIVE
BEHAVIOR"--

--IS
TALKING
TO ME LIKE
THAT--!

CHAPTER THREE

HIT *SIXTH FLOOR*, PLEASE.

HEY--

--QUIT *SHOVING*--

--WHAT'S THE *LOAD LIMIT* ON THIS THING?

--GOING *DOWN*, MR. TYLER?

2 3 4 5 6 7 8 9 1

--SO THEN *HE* SAYS--

--EVER TELL YOU I'M *CLAUSTRO-PHOBIC*?

--MAN, I *HATE* SHIFT CHANGES--

--SHOULDA TAKEN THE *STAIRS*--

--THE TERM *CATTLE CAR* COMES TO MIND--

--ABOUT THAT *BOOMER* FROM A COUPLE OF NIGHTS AGO--

--SO THEN *I* SAY--

HEARD FROM THE *TECHIES* DOWNSTAIRS--

--Y'KNOW THAT *MEMORY MODULE* WE PICKED UP OFF THAT LAST *BOOMER*?

YEAH.

TURNS OUT THOSE *GEEKS* IN *COMP/ ANALYSIS* FINALLY *DECRYPTED* THE DAMN THING, MAN.

WELL, WHOOP-DEE-FRIGGIN'-DOO.

GLAD TO HEAR IT.

HERE WE ARE--FIFTH FLOOR, *COMP/ ANALYSIS*--

HOLD THE DOOR, PLEASE!

UH, THIS IS MY *FLOOR....*!

THE **SKORPION 19** WAS THE LAST GASP OF FINE EUROPEAN MECHATRONICS, BEFORE **GENOM'S** BOOMER TECHNOLOGY FINALLY DROVE THE EUROS OUT OF THE FIELD.

IT WAS DESIGNED AS AN **ANTHOLOGY INTELLIGENCE,** ABLE TO DISPERSE ITS LIMITED AWARENESS THOUGH A JURY-RIGGED NETWORK OF SUBUNIT **MECHS** AND **COMPUTERS.**

COMPARED TO THE HUMAN-DERIVED COMPLEXITY OF GENOM'S **BOOMERS,** THE SKORPION IS **CRUDE** AND **PATHETIC,** A BARELY COGNITIVE HEAP OF OBSOLETE MACHINERY.

BUT IT'S ALMOST **UN-BEATABLE** AT THE FEW **SPECIALIZED** TASKS IT WAS BUILT TO HANDLE.

A MECHANICAL **IDIOT SAVANT,** YOU MIGHT SAY.

--VASHNEVSKAYA, YOUR **COMLINK IMPLANT** SHOULD BE ABLE TO RECEIVE THE SKORPION'S **ENCRYPTED TRANSMISSIONS** NOW.

CAN YOU **HEAR** IT?

THE SKORPION COMMUNICATES VIA *"AUDIO SAMPLES"* TAKEN FROM VARIOUS MEDIA SOURCES.

THIS MIGHT BE A BIT **JAR-RING,** AT FIRST...

NAH, NOT **REALLY.**

IT JUST SOUNDS LIKE **REALLY** PRETENTIOUS AUDIO-FORMAT **PERFORMANCE ART...**

...DON' CHOO KNOW I'M LOCO?

ONCE AGAIN, I'M FACING A SLAVERING HORDE OF COMBAT BOOMERS.

BUT *THIS* TIME, THEY'LL BE ON MY SIDE.

I HOPE.

TWO NIGHTS AGO, THE SKORPION TELLS ME, A *HOSTILE* BOOMER RIPPED OFF SOME *VITAL ELEMENT* OF THE MECH'S ANTHOLOGY INTELLIGENCE.

SOME *MEMORY MODULE,* STUFFED WITH DATA *CRITICAL* TO OUR DARING MISSION.

EVENTUALLY, THE MODULE ENDED UP IN THE HANDS OF MEGATOKYO'S *HAPLESS ADVANCED POLICE.*

NOW WE'RE PRESSING A STOLEN COMBAT BOOMER INTO SERVICE TO HELP *RECOVER* IT.

NOTHING'S MORE PLEASINGLY *IRONIC* THAN USING A *GENOM PRODUCT* AGAINST ITS *MAKERS...*

--PUTTING DOWN A *DOMESTIC INSURGENCY?* PLANNING SOME *TERRITORIAL EXPANSION* BY FORCE?

OR JUST LOOKING TO SPICE UP YOUR *JANE'S DAY MILITARY PARADE?* WELL, THE *HEAVY-DUTY BU-12C COMBAT BOOMER* IS JUST WHAT--

HE-AP 85mm

VIDEO SAMPLE

--GOOD NEWS ON THAT *MEMORY MODULE* THINGIE, SYLIA!

WE SHOULD HAVE A *COMPLETE* DOWNLOAD FROM IT, IN AN HOUR OR TWO!

NEAT, HUH?

EXCELLENT, NENE.

WOW!

NENE ACTUALLY DOING SOMETHING *USEFUL?*

I'M *BLOWN AWAY!*

HUH?

HMM...FILES ON THE CREATION OF *BOOMER ARTIFICIAL INTELLIGENCE?* THAT'S CURIOUS...

IT'S *NENE?*

THIS MIGHT CONCERN SOME OF THE MORE *SHADOWY* ASPECTS OF MY FATHER'S WORK, PERHAPS...

SO, NENE, YOU *CAN* SAFELY GET ACCESS TO THIS DATA, RIGHT...?

OH, COME *ON,* SYLIA!

I'M *LORD* AND *MASTER* OF THE ADP COMPUTER SYSTEM!

IN *SECRET,* OF COURSE.

MOVE *IT,* PEOPLE!

--DURING MY *COFFEE BREAK,* OF COURSE--

--*ANOTHER* BOOMER--?

HUH?

LEA AND I'LL HANDLE THE *GROUND TROOPS*--

--YOU TWO HELP DISPATCH THE *HELOS,* OKAY?

--SOUNDS LIKE A *MEAN* ONE, THIS TIME...

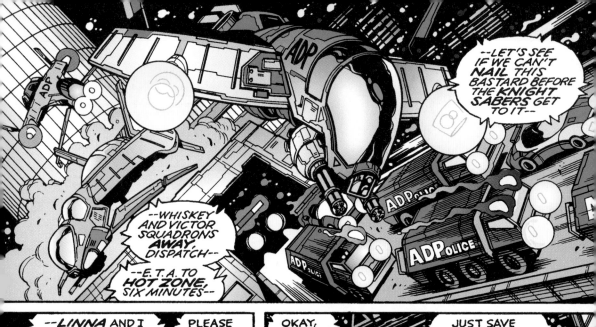

--LET'S SEE IF WE CAN'T *NAIL* THIS *BASTARD* BEFORE THE *KNIGHT SABERS* GET TO IT--

--WHISKEY AND VICTOR SQUADRONS *AWAY*, DISPATCH--

--E.T.A. TO *HOT ZONE*, SIX MINUTES--

--*LINNA* AND I ARE HEADING OUT NOW...I'LL LEAVE THE *MOTOROID* HERE FOR YOU, *PRISS*.

PLEASE *HURRY*, ALL RIGHT?

YOU GUYS *READY* YET--?

OKAY, *OKAY!*

PLEASE *EXCUSE* ME FOR HAVING SOME *VESTIGE* OF A LIFE *OUTSIDE* THE KNIGHT SABERS--!

JUST SAVE SOME *BOOMER* FOR ME AND MY *MOTOSLAVE*, OKAY?

HEY, THERE'S THE *ADPOLICE!*♪♫

MAYBE WE WON'T NEED TO *INTERVENE*, AFTER ALL!

SNORT YEAH, *RIGHT.*

WHUP   WHUP   WH

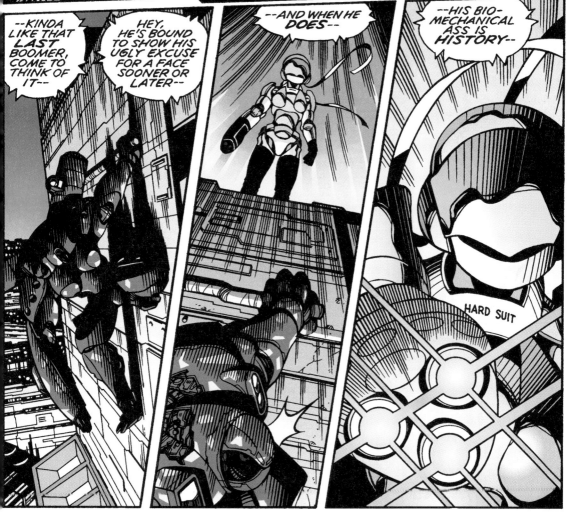

FWOOOSH

CHOOM CHOOM

CHOOM
CHOOM
CHOOM
CHOOM
CHOOM

"MY FATHER, USING A SOMEWHAT *RADICAL* TECHNIQUE, DERIVED THE FORM OF ARTIFICIAL INTELLIGENCE USED IN *BOOMERS*--

"--FROM A *HUMAN* MODEL, A HUMAN *BRAIN*.

"BUT FOR ITS *COMBAT* BOOMERS--

"--GENOM UTILIZED A DRASTICALLY *SIMPLIFIED* VERSION OF HIS WORK--

FWOOOSH

OUR **DECOY BOOMER** DID ITS JOB JUST FINE.

ONLY **NONCOMBATANTS** LEFT TO DEAL WITH, AT LEAST FOR A FEW MINUTES.

THE **SKORPION'S** SUBUNITS DEPLOY SOME **NONLETHAL** HARDWARE--

--NERVE GEL, ELECTROSHOCK AND **KINETIC** STUN ROUNDS--

POONT

--PLUS ENOUGH **SAVORY** PEPPERGAS TO KEEP THESE CIV VIES **DOWN** AND **OUT** UNTIL WE LEAVE.

AH, THE **PROUD GLORY** OF **BATTLE**--

--SO **STARTLINGLY** EVIDENT IN THE VALIANT TASK OF **GASSING** OFFICE WORKERS--

--**ALL FORCES,** THIS IS ADPOLICE HEADQUARTERS--

--WE'RE **UNDER ATTACK**--!

REPEAT, **UNDER ATTACK**--

THE SUBUNITS HAVE **SEALED** OFF THE ELE-VATORS AND STAIRWELLS.

NOW, **WHERE** DID THESE PEOPLE HIDE THE **MEMORY MODULE**?

KSHANG KSHANG KSHANG

KRUMF

AH, **HERE**...DOOR LOOKS A LITTLE **SMALL,** THOUGH.

TOO **BAD.**

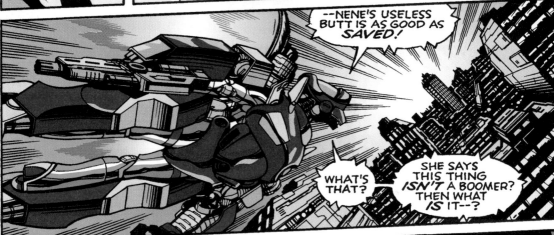

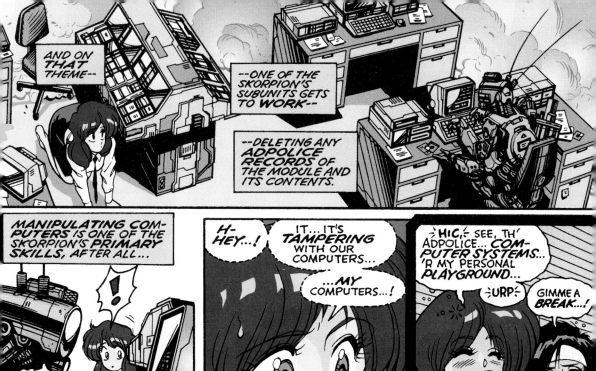

AND ON *THAT* THEME—

—ONE OF THE SKORPION'S SUBUNITS GETS TO *WORK*—

—DELETING ANY ADPOLICE RECORDS OF THE MODULE AND ITS CONTENTS.

MANIPULATING COMPUTERS IS ONE OF THE SKORPION'S *PRIMARY* SKILLS, AFTER ALL...

H—HEY...!

IT... IT'S *TAMPERING* WITH OUR COMPUTERS...

...*MY* COMPUTERS...!

—HIC—SEE, TH' ADPOLICE... *COMPUTER* SYSTEMS... 'R MY PERSONAL *PLAYGROUND*...

—URP—

GIMME A *BREAK*...!

VIDEO SAMPLE

NOBODY—HNNH—MESSES WITH *MY* MACHINES—

—HFF—

BWA HA HA HA!

SKRASH

HOW'S *THAT,* CREEP—

HUH?

VREEE

EEEYAAA!

WHIRRR

CHALK UP *ANOTHER* TIMELY RESCUE!

WHAT THE HELL?

ALWAYS PLAYING THE *DAMSEL IN DISTRESS,* HUH, NENE?

THAT'S DEFINITE-LY NOT ADPOLICE-ISSUE HARDWARE!

SHUT UP!!

THERE'S A *BIGGER* ONE BACK THERE!

STOP PICKING ON *ME* AND GIVE THE *BAD GUYS* SOME ABUSE, OKAY?

WHATEVER THE MECH IS--

--THE SKORPION ISN'T CARRYING ANY ORDNANCE HEAVY ENOUGH TO *DEAL* WITH IT.

BUT THAT'S *FINE*--

--THE SKORPION AND I ARE OLD HANDS AT IMPROVISING SOLUTIONS--!

SSSHHHREEE

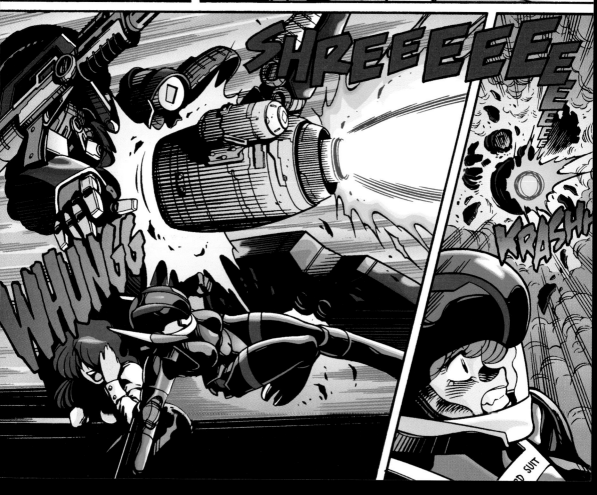

SHREEEEE

WHUNGG

KRASH

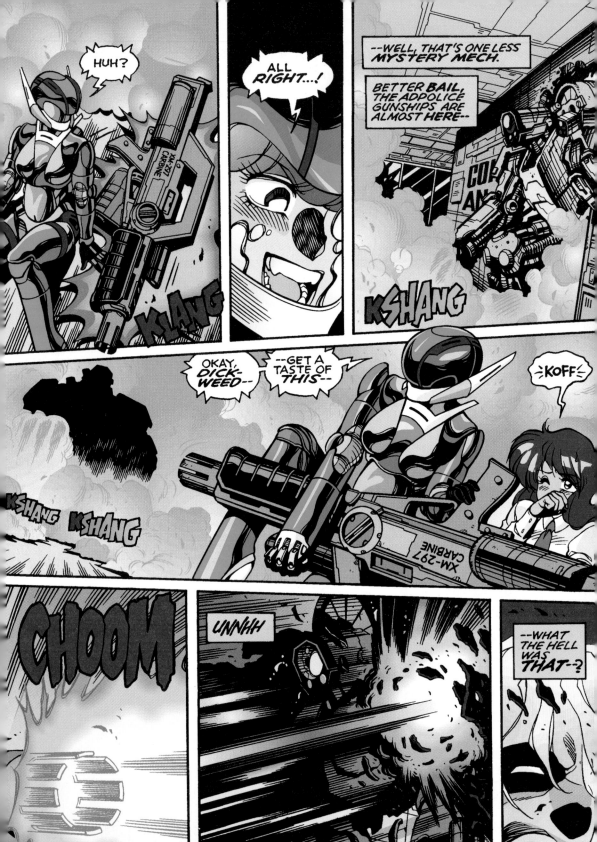

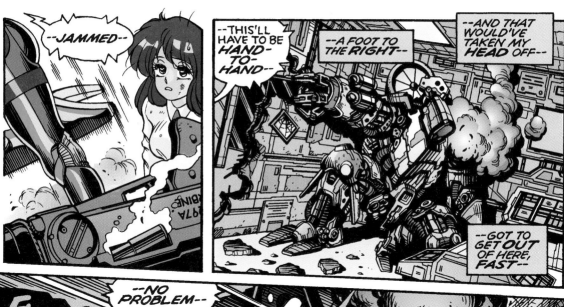

CHAPTER FOUR

"...BUT THERE'S NO *TRACE* OF IT NOW."

"OUR *GUESTS* TOOK THE TIME TO WIPE IT FROM OUR COMPUTERS, APPARENTLY."

"IN FACT, YOUR GIRLFRIEND *NENE* SPOTTED A MECH MESSING AROUND AT A TERMINAL..."

"DAMN! NENE WASN'T *HURT*, WAS SHE?"

"NO, THE ONLY WOUND SHE SUFFERED WAS TO HER *ADPOLICE PRIDE,* LIKE THE REST OF US."

"GOOD. HATE TO THINK OF A *PIECE* LIKE HER GETTING MESSED UP...!"

WELL. SPEAKING OF *PIECES,* LEON...

...DID ANYONE TELL YOU THAT A *KNIGHT SABER* DROPPED BY TO TUSSLE WITH THE MECHS?

YEAH, AND GOT HERSELF *MINIGUNNED* TO PIECES, I HEARD.

THAT'S ONE LESS *VIGILANTE BABE* IN HIGH-HEELED ARMOR, HUH?

WHUP WHUP WHUP

HARD TO SAY. WORD IS, SOME KIND OF *CANDY APPLE RED* MECH FLEW OFF WITH THE BODY...

ALSO EVADING OUR POOR HELO JOCKEYS, OF COURSE.

MAN, THIS HAS BEEN ONE *WRETCHED* WEEK FOR THE ADPOLICE...

...HELL, IT'S BEEN A WRETCHED WEEK FOR PRETTY MUCH *EVERY-BODY...*

THEY'RE *BADLY* OVEREXTENDED, QUINCY.

JUST UP *YOUR* OFFER BY, SAY, FIVE YUAN A SHARE PLUS SOME MUNICIPAL BONDS...

...AND YOU'LL OUTBID THEM *SAFELY* AND WITHOUT *EXCESS,* OKAY?

WHUP WHUP WHUP WHUP

WITNESS THE PROCESS OF *DECISION MAKING* AT MIGHTY *GENOM!*

FINE, QUINCY. *YOU'RE* THE EXECUTIVE BOARD CHAIRMAN, I'M JUST THE *STRATEGIC ADVISOR.*

YOU CAN *LISTEN* TO MY "LEARNED COUNSEL," OR JUST DISREGARD IT.

THE DECISION'S *YOURS.*

LISTEN AS THE ORGANIC EXECUTIVES SOLICIT *BRILLIANT ADVICE* FROM THEIR *"INTELLECTUAL ASSETS"...*

...AND THEN FREELY *IGNORE* IT!

HIDEBOUND, PATHETIC OLD *DINOSAURS...!*

WHY DO THEY ASK *QUESTIONS* IF THEY CAN'T DEAL WITH THE *ANSWERS...?*

OH, IT'S JUST A *HUMAN* THING. THEY HAVE TO MAKE A TOKEN DECISION OR TWO ON THEIR *OWN...*

...JUST TO *REASSURE* THEM- SELVES THAT THEY'RE STILL IN CONTROL...

CONSIDERING THAT THEY DECIDE WHETHER WE *LIVE* OR *DIE*, I'D SAY THE ORGANICS ARE *DEFINITELY* STILL IN CONTROL...!

HEY!

WHAT ABOUT THE THREAT FROM *OUT- SIDE?*

AS IN *VASHNEVSKAYA* AND HIS ADORABLE LITTLE MECH? GET *SERIOUS...*

HEY, THEY'VE RETRIEVED THAT PESKY *MODULE...*

...NO DOUBT THEY'VE PREPPED TONS OF *NASTY* HARDWARE...

...AND ARE ON THE VERGE OF A *PAROXYSM* OF *APOCALYPTIC MAYHEM!*

EITHER THAT, OR THEY'RE SITTING AROUND DOING *NOTHING.*

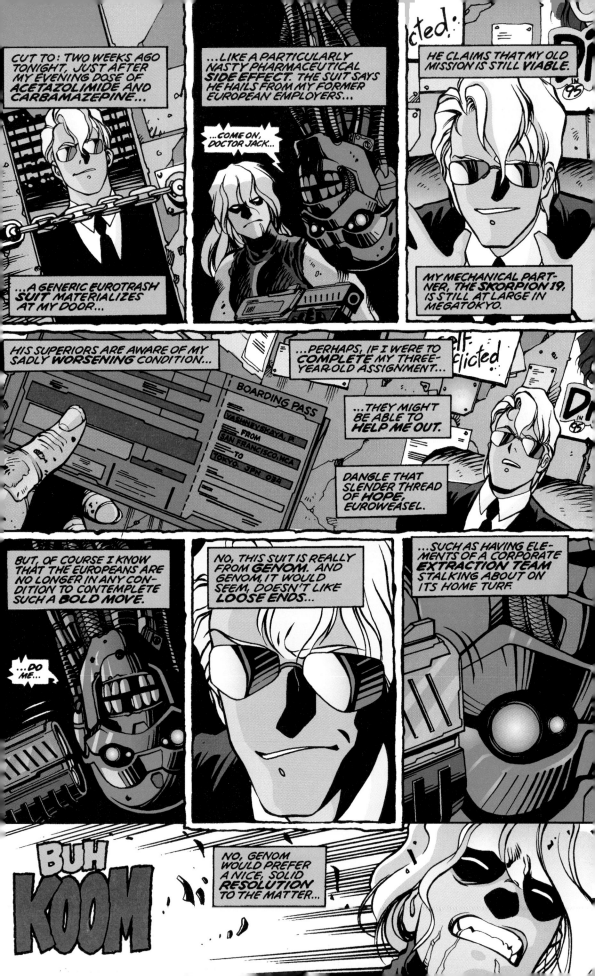

I'M *IMPRESSED*...

...THEY ACTUALLY OBTAINED COPIES OF FATHER'S *PROTESTS* TO THE EXECUTIVE BOARD...!

HEY, SIS...

...I'VE FINISHED THE REPAIRS ON THE *MOTOSLAVE*, OR *MOTOROID*, WHATEVER...

...IT'S STILL IN BAD SHAPE BUT IT SHOULD HOLD TOGETHER FOR A *LITTLE* WHILE...

SO YOU GUYS SHOULD BE ABLE TO GET SOME *USE* OUT OF... UHHHH...

I MEAN, UM...

UHHHH...

WHY, MACKIE, YOU *LECH*...!

TRY NOT TO GET ANY *DROOL* ON ME, OK?

?

PRISS--!

WHAAAT?

UH, BE BACK IN A LITTLE WHILE--

--GOTTA GO *FUEL UP* THE TRUCK--

RIO

HEY, WHAT'RE *YOU* GETTING UPSET ABOUT, NENE?

HMFF.

GOOD WORK, NENE.

THESE *DECRYPTED FILES* MAKE IT CLEAR EXACTLY WHAT THESE MECHS ARE *DOING* IN MEGATOKYO.

AS *INSANE* AN OBJECTIVE AS IT MAY BE...

UM, GLAD TO BE OF SERVICE, SYLIA...

...FOR *ONCE*...

...I KNOW WHAT THEY'RE AFTER.

MY MECHANICAL FRIEND, THE *SKORPION 19*, SPENT THE LAST THREE YEARS IN AN *ORGY* OF INFORMATION GATHERING.

IT CONDUCTED *ENDLESS* HOURS OF AUDIO AND VIDEO SURVEILLANCE WITH ITS SUB-UNIT MECHS.

IT MONITORED EVERY CONCEIVABLE *MEDIA OUTLET*, FROM MAIN-STREAM NEWS FEEDS TO ANARCHIST BULLETIN BOARDS.

SKORPION™

IN TIME, IT TAPPED INTO EVERY METAPHORICAL EXIT, TOLL PLAZA, AND TRAFFIC CIRCLE OF MEGA-TOKYO'S *INFORMATION SUPERHIGHWAY.*

--INTERESTING RUMOR ABOUT GENOM--

--A COVERT PLANNING GROUP--

--DR. STINGRAY, CREATOR OF--

JUDGING FROM THESE FILES, THEY'RE EVIDENTLY PLANNING AN *"EXTRACTION ATTEMPT"*--

--WITH VIRTUALLY *NO* CHANCE OF SUCCESS--

--TARGETING ONE OF GENOM'S *"INTELLECTUAL ASSETS"*--

--PENETRATING THOUSANDS OF *COMPUTER SYSTEMS,* SIFTING THROUGH *TERA-BYTES* OF *ELECTRONIC* GARBAGE TO PIECE TOGETHER A *WORKABLE MEANS* OF ACHIEVING OUR GOAL--

--SIGNIFICANT ASPECT OF DR. STINGRAY'S WORK--

--STINGRAY IS SURVIVED BY DAUGHTER SYLIA, TWELVE, AND--

--BOOMER'S FORM OF ARTIFICIAL INTELLIGENCE--

--THEY'RE *"NEURO-LOGICALLY ENHANCED,"* HUH?

YES. THESE INDIVIDUALS ARE *ARTIFICIAL BEINGS* SIMILAR, IN A WAY, TO *BOOMERS...*

...THEY'RE YET *ANOTHER* PRODUCT OF MY FATHER'S WORK...

HEH... NICE *PANTIES,* PRISS...

BRMMM

--SPLICING IN THE DATA FROM THE LOST MEMORY MODULE, THE SKORPION INFODUMPS TO ME VIA AUDIO AND VIDEO SAMPLES ASSEMBLED DURING ITS YEARS OF RECONNAISSANCE.

THE SAMPLING TECHNIQUE'S SOMEWHAT ANNOYING, BUT YOU CAN GET USED TO IT.

VIDEO SAMPLE

--CRITICAL PART OF STINGRAY'S WORK FOR GENOM WAS HIS REPLICATION OF HUMAN CONSCIOUSNESS IN "BOOMER TECHNOLOGY".

--INSTEAD, MY FATHER TOOK THE ROUTE OF TRYING TO DIRECTLY CONVERT HUMAN BRAIN INTO A SOFTWARE ANALOG--

JUST GIVE ME THE SHORT FORM, OK?

VIDEO SAMPLE

--STINGRAY'S SO-CALLED "NEUROPHAGE," WHICH WAS AN EXPERIMENTAL BIO-COMPUTER-CONTROLLED MOLECULAR MACHINE DESIGNED TO BE INTRODUCED, MILLIONS AT A TIME, INTO A LIVING BRAIN--

"NEURO-PHAGE"

VIDEO SAMPLE

--EACH NEUROPHAGE WOULD DISASSEMBLE A NEURON, MOLECULE BY MOLECULE, AND REPLACE IT WITH A BIOCOMPUTERIZED DUPLICATE--

--WEIRDLY ENOUGH, HEARING DESCRIPTIONS OF TINY MANMADE CRITTERS CHEWING THEIR WAY THROUGH BRAIN TISSUE--

--JUST MAKES ME HUNGRY--

EVENTUALLY, ALL TISSUE WOULD BE REPLACED BY A MASS OF NEUROPHAGES THAT WOULD MIMIC THE OPERATION OF THE ORIGINAL BRAIN--

NEURON

"NEURO-PHAGE" (NOT TO SCALE)

--GRADUALLY INSINUATING THEMSELVES THROUGH THE BRAIN'S NEURAL NETWORK

--REPORTEDLY, STINGRAY WAS ANGERED BY GENOM'S RECKLESS EXPERIMENTATION--

--FAVORED LIMITED TESTING OF NEUROPHAGES ON--

--RETAINING MOST OF THE SUBJECT'S COGNITIVE, BEHAVIORAL AND EMOTIONAL TRAITS--

IT'S SENSELESS IDIOCY TO CONTINUE WITH THIS MISSION, I KNOW.

BUT AS FUTILE, MEANINGLESS, AND EVEN SUICIDAL AS IT HAPPENS TO BE...

...THIS IS MY JOB.

--COMING AFTER US, OF COURSE!

WE ARE THE ONLY NEUROLOGICALLY ENHANCED INTELLECTS IN MEGA-TOKYO, AFTER ALL...

ARE YOU CERTAIN? YOU'VE HEARD THE RUMORS...

...THE MECH MIGHT HAVE ROOTED OUT ANOTHER AUGMENTED THINKER...

...A ROGUE "INTELLECTUAL ASSET," IF YOU WILL...

--WITH AN ATTACK ON GENOM TOWER IMMINENT, YOUR HARDSUIT'S SENSOR SUITES AND SURVEILLANCE GEAR WILL BE CRITICAL, NENE.

AFTER LAST NIGHT, ARE YOU FEELING UP TO THIS...?

DON'T WORRY ABOUT ME, SYLIA!

I'M READY FOR ANYTHING!

EXCEPT A FIGHT, MAYBE...

HUSH, LINNA.

--*OR* HE'S ON HIS WAY HERE.

EITHER WAY, THE ISSUE WILL BE RESOLVED *SHORTLY*--

--NOT TO MENTION *VIOLENTLY*--

--I GIVE THE *SKORPION* THE FINAL ELEMENT OF ITS *ACTIVATION CODE*--

--PERVERSELY ENOUGH, A QUOTE FROM THE *MARQUIS DE SADE*--!

"OH, WHAT ACTION SO *VOLUPTUOUS* AS *DESTRUCTION!*"

ONCE *MACKIE* COMES BACK, WE'LL HEAD TO A MONITORING POST CLOSE BY *GENOM TOWER*--

--IN CASE WE NEED TO *INTERVENE*--

WHAT?

ARE YOU **CRAZY?**

"THERE IS NO *ECSTASY* LIKE THE ONE WE TASTE--"

IF THIS BASTARD'S GONNA ATTACK *GENOM*, WHY EVEN *THINK* OF STOPPING HIM--?

PRISS...

INNOCENT PEOPLE COULD BE HURT. WE HAVE TO—

HEY, I WANT HIM *DEAD*... BUT IF HE TAKES OUT SOME *GENOM* SCUMBAGS FIRST, *ALL THE BETTER!*

PRISS, THIS MECH MIGHT TRY TO *DESTROY* ITS PREY, INSTEAD OF CAPTURING THEM...

...WE COULD *ALL* BE IN DANGER IF—

WHKROOM

"WHEN WE GIVE OURSELVES OVER TO THIS DIVINE INFAMY!"

CHOOM
CHOOM

RMBLL

KOFF!

W-WHAT THE HELL--?!

OWWW--!

MY LEGS-- I'M PINNED--

--SOME-BODY *HELP* ME--

--HOLD ON, NENE--

THEY'VE COME AFTER *US*--

WHSHY

SHIIIINGG

EVERYTHING I'VE EVER SAID ABOUT YOU--

--I TAKE IT ALL *BACK*--!

ALL RIGHT, *LINNA!*

CHOOM

--M-MECH'S *GOTTA* BE RUNNING THOSE BOOMERS BY *REMOTE LINK*--!

SHOULD BE ABLE TO *JAM* THE *SIGNAL*--

--OR *OVERRIDE* IT--

--B-BUT THE SIGNAL'S *FREQUENCY-HOPPING*--!

N-NO-- *PLEASE*--

--DON'T--

--DON'T--

SHRAKK

THUDD

KRCHAK

HUHH HUHH

SHOULD'VE... *EXPECTED* THIS...

HEY, NOBODY'S *PERFECT*, SYLIA...

...NOT EVEN AN *AUGMENTED INTELLECT* LIKE YOUR-SELF...

SORRY, SYLIA...

...I *SCREWED UP AGAIN*...

KNIGHT SABERS

DIDN'T HAVE TO GO TO *GENOM TOWER* TO FIND ONE OF THE *NEUROLOGICALLY ENHANCED*, AFTER ALL...

...JUST HAD TO LOOK FOR *YOU*...!

DADDY JUST COULDN'T *STOP* HIMSELF, COULD HE?

...NICE GUY, EXPERIMENTING ON HIS OWN CHILDREN...!

WHY, I EVEN READ *ALL* ABOUT IT IN YOUR NOT-SO-PRIVATE RECORDS, SYLIA...

STINGRAY HAD TO GIVE HIS *LITTLE GIRL* SOME VERSION OF HIS *NEUROPHAGE TREATMENT*...

VIDEO SAMPLE

"...TO AID YOU IN THIS...

"I HAVE GIVEN YOU AND YOUR BROTHER CERTAIN...*GIFTS*, YOU MIGHT SAY.

--SKORPION'S BEEN *TRACKING* YOU FOR YEARS--

--KEEPING A CAREFUL WATCH ON YOUR *GOOFY CRUSADE*--

--UNTIL WE COULD *REEL YOU IN.*

LISTEN, YOU MERCENARY *BASTARD*--

--MY *"CRUSADE"* IS ALL THAT'S STOPPING GENOM FROM--

I'M SURE THAT THE VERY *THOUGHT* OF A COUPLE OF CUTE GIRLS PRANCING AROUND IN *HIGH-HEELED ARMOR* IS GONNA PUT THE *FEAR OF GOD*--

--INTO THE MOST POWERFUL COMMERCIAL ENTITY IN *HUMAN HISTORY*--!

D-*DAMN IT*--!

"CHOOSING TO *ALTER* YOU HAS BEEN BY FAR THE MOST *PAINFUL* DECISION I'VE EVER HAD TO--"

YEAH, *RIGHT.*

YOU SAID YOU *HATED* GENOM!

HUKK— WORD TO...THE *WISE*, GIRLS...

...THE SKORPION'S... *FINISHED*...

GUCHK!

...BUT IT'S... PROGRAMMED... TO *SPOIL-SPORT*...

KOFF—

...WIRED TO... *SELF-DESTRUCT*...

...SPECTACU-LARLY...

...SO... HKK—

...UNLESS... YOU'D CARE... TO ACCOMPANY ME... TO *HELL*...

UM, *SYLIA*...?

FROM WHAT MY SENSORS ARE PICKING UP, HE'S *NOT* KIDDING...!

...YOU'D BEST... GET THE *FLOCK*... OUT OF HERE...

OH, *MAN*--!

I CAN'T *BELIEVE* THIS!

LEAVE 'EM ALONE FOR *TEN* MINUTES--

--AND JUST *SEE* WHAT HAPPENS--!

DAMN... GETTING *DISEMBOWELED* BY AN ARMOR-PIERCING CANNON ROUND--

--CUT THAT *SEIZURE* RIGHT OFF--

--SHOULD LET MY NEURO-LOGIST KNOW ABOUT *THIS* ANTI-SEIZURE TREATMENT--

--WHAT *HAPPENED* TO YOU GUYS--?!

...DON'T ASK...

I SAVED THE DAY! ♪

MACKIE!

WE'RE GETTING *OUT* OF HERE, *NOW--*

--*DEATH*--

--IT'S THE ONE *SURE CURE* FOR WHAT AILS YOU--

HUH?

HEY, SIS, WHAT'S *THAT?*

NOTHING I LIKE BETTER THAN BEING *HAULED AROUND* LIKE A SACK OF GROCERIES...

HURRY UP--!

THIS ISN'T SO BAD

MAYBE I SHOULD'VE

A LITTLE *SOUVENIR* FOR OUR TROUBLES, YOU MIGHT SAY--

DONE THIS

SOONER

POP

MANGA VIDEO

If you've enjoyed this Manga Book, you'll love the animated movies and series released on the Manga Video label. Many of them are based on Japanese comics (*Crying Freeman*, *Akira* and *Battle Angel Alita* to name but a few), but all of them prove that there are no limits to animation with their imaginings of post-apocalyptic hells, bio-engineered mechanoids, other-worldly nightmarish fiends, wide-eyed babes, devouring tentacles and neon techno-mad cities. The range of Manga Videos is available from all good video and record stores including Virgin, HMV, Woolworths, WH Smith, Our Price, Playhouse and Forbidden Planet, and there are new titles out every month.

To find out more, join the Official Manga Club and receive a quarterly newsletter, as well as discounts on Manga Books and selected Manga Videos, free entry to competitions, free Manga merchandise and a free copy of the Manga Video Collectors Edition (retail price £6.99) — all for only £10 a year. Call 0181 563 2028 for an application form, or fill out and send off the form available in every Manga Video.

Up-to-date news on Manga is also available on the Internet by accessing **http://www.mangavid.co.uk/mangavid/** or **http://www.mangapub.co.uk/mangapub/**

If you're new to Japanese animation, then these are some of the most popular titles:

AKIRA
(15 cert., 124 mins approx., #IWCV 1001, RRP: £13.99)

Drug-crazed biker gangs battle for high-speed supremacy in the neonscape of a nightmare future Tokyo: this is the setting for the biggest, most expensively produced and most famous manga release ever.

UROTSUKIDOJI: LEGEND OF THE OVERFIEND
(18 cert, 104 mins approx., #MANV 1008, RRP: £13.99)

& LEGEND OF THE DEMON WOMB
(18 cert, 83 mins approx., #MANV 1009, RRP: £13.99)

Terrifying masterpieces beyond the limits of animation as demonic lusts and supernatural ultraviolence explode into physical reality.

THE GUYVER
(12 episodes, RRP: £5.99, all approx. 30 mins)

An epic science fiction adventure which explores the fusion of man and machine, and delves into the origins of the human species itself.

DOMINION TANK POLICE
(8 videos - 2 @ 68 mins approx., RRP: £13.99 and 6 @ 30 mins approx., RRP: £5.99)

Rioutous tales of police, pollution and heavy weaponry from cybermeister Masamune Shirow, set in a world where the cops are more dangerous than the crooks!

FIST OF THE NORTH STAR
(18 cert, 112 mins approx., #MANV 1001, RRP: £13.99)

A grim-faced lone warrior, armed with the power of an age-old martial arts discipline, wanders the ruined and irradiated wastelands of a post-apocalyptic nuclear hell, searching for the woman he loves and protecting mankind's final chance for survival.

PATLABOR
(PG cert, 99 mins approx., #MANV 1080, RRP: £13.99)

An incredibly animated science fiction drama set against a tale of danger and hi-tech revenge as the police force of 1999 enlist advanced pilot-operated robots to combat crime.